ISBN 0-85116-644-X

£4.99

SEEING IS BELIEVING

WE'RE REALLY IN TROUBLE — WE HAVEN'T DONE OUR HOMEWORK!

WE'LL GET DETENTION.

I'VE GOT A PLAN — WE'LL MAKE TEACHER THINK HIS SIGHT'S WONKY. WATCH — I'LL DEMONSTRATE.

Then—

HELLO AGAIN, TEACHER.

WILFRID? IS THAT YOU?

IT WORKED A TREAT.

NO, IT COULDN'T HAVE BEEN — I MUST HAVE BEEN SEEING THINGS!

Soon—

BRRRR!

SHIVER

EXERCISING? FATTY? I DON'T BELIEVE IT!

I'M TRYING TO SLIM, TEACHER.

THWACK! THWACK!

THWACK! THWACK!

I MUST RUB MY EYES — I DON'T BELIEVE WHAT THEY SEE!

JUST GET RID OF THESE.

RUB!

RUB!

THROW!

So—

WHAT ARE YOU DOING WITH THAT BALLOON SMIFFY?

DEFLATE!

INFLATE!

WAH! I'M REALLY SEEING THINGS!

TUG!

NOW TEACHER WILL THINK WE'VE DONE ALL OUR HOMEWORK.

"POLL" POSITION!

IT'S TIME THIS SCHOOL HAD A HEAD PUPIL...

THAT'S THE JOB FOR ME!

NO, ME!

ME!

SPLAT
SPLAT
SPLAT

I D-DON'T THINK THEY TH-THOUGHT V-VERY M-M-MUCH OF IT!

PEOPLE WHO WANT TO WIN VOTES KISS BABIES.

Soon —

VOTE FOR ME AND GET FREE GRUB!

SOUNDS GREAT — WHERE'S THE GRUB?

LEFTOVERS FROM SCHOOL DINNERS — THERE'S PLENTY!

SCHOOL KITCHEN BACK DOOR

DOES THIS MEAN YOU WON'T VOTE FOR ME?

Next day —

BEFORE YOU VOTE FOR HEAD PUPIL...

WHICH WILL BE ME!

ME!

ME!

... READ THIS!

SCHOOL NOTICE BOARD

LIST OF A HEAD PUPIL'S DUTIES
*
OFFICIAL SCHOOL DINNER TASTER
*
TEACHER'S PET
*
FIRST TO SCHOOL —LAST OUT
*
HARD SUMS TEST PILOT

ME!

ME!

STOP IT! THERE WILL BE AN ELECTION TOMORROW — THE PERSON WITH MOST VOTES WILL BE HEAD PUPIL!

BOOMF

THUMP

THUD

The election campaign begins —

VOTE FOR ME AND I'LL SEE YOU GET LOTS OF HARD SUMS AND EXAMS — WHAT DO YOU THINK OF THAT THEN, EH?

NURSERY

WAY IN

PUCKER

WAH-H!

DONK

DONK

HOWL!

TAKE THAT! THAT'LL TEACH YOU NOT TO SCARE BABIES WITH THAT HORRID FACE!

BOAK!

URGH!

GLAARGH!

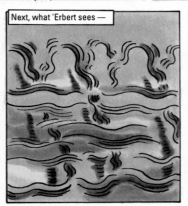

Next, what 'Erbert sees —

VOTE FOR ME — I'LL SEE YOU'RE WELL-TREATED.

THAT'S ABOUT ALL YOU'LL SEE!

EVERYONE VOTE!

AND THE HEAD PUPIL IS . . .

. . . WINSTON!

WINSTON

FOR HE'S A JOLLY GOOD PUSSY . . .

H-HOW DID THIS HAPPEN?

WINSTON

WINSTON

WINSTON

WINSTON

PANTO TIME

WITH A CRUNCH AND A CLOUT,
OH, DEAR ME – POOR TOOTS!
'COS WINSTON'S THE STAR,
OF THE SHOW **PUSS IN BOOTS.**

The BASH STREET KIDS in SPORTING STRIFE

"EVERYONE outside!" said Teacher. His voice sounded strange to the kids' ears. It sounded even more peculiar to their noses and particularly weird to their eyebrows.

"What did he say?" Danny was stunned (Sidney had just thrown one of Olive's sponge cakes at him).

"It's school sports day today!" said Cuthbert pointedly, as Fatty used him as a javelin and threw him out the open window.

Cuthbert landed nose first on the playing field. "Dow! Bat durt!" he said thickly. "Who cares? It's a new school record!" replied Danny thinly.

"Let's start with the 3-legged race," said Teacher, handing out some string in a very ropey manner. The kids tied their legs together with all the skill and dexterity of a hippo wearing boxing gloves. Smiffy even tied his own legs together — he would have been last if the myopic, short-sighted and blind as a bat 'Erbert hadn't tied his leg to a goalpost he had mistaken for Plug.

Fatty's waistline was first across the finish line as he and Spotty beat Danny and Wilfrid by a short head (Wilfrid's, actually). "The winners!" Teacher cried. No wonder he cried — you'd cry too if Fatty was standing on your toes!

FINISH

DAB! DAB!

STOMP

FLATTEN

Before you could say, "You stupid, fat, lardbucket!" Fatty had heated up a discus to use as a frying pan. "I'm making an omelette!" he said, his voice cracking in time with the eggs.

"You stupid, fat . . ." began Danny. Too late! Fatty had eaten the omelette.

CRACK

SIZZLE

SIZZLE

"It's time for the sack race," said Plug darkly — the other kids had tied his sack over his head to hide his hideous fizzog. "Ready, steady . . . GLUB!" said teacher wetly (Danny had swapped his starting pistol for a water pistol).

Fatty was now almost completely round and he began to bounce. He bounced over the rest of the kids and won easily.

"Fatty wins again!" said Teacher flatly (Fatty had landed on him). The kids were not happy.

FINISH

"We're not happy!" they said. They grabbed Fatty and pinned him to the ground with glue. "We'll teach you to bounce past us!" they said in unison, together and all at once.

GLUE

SQUIRT

Plan and Simple

I'VE GOT A GREAT PLAN TO GET OUT OF SCHOOLWORK TOMORROW . . .

. . . AW, STOP MESSING ABOUT AND LISTEN TO MY PLAN . . .

WE'RE GOING TO MAKE TEACHER THINK IT'S STILL NIGHT — ALL DAY! NO WORK FOR US TODAY!

BEDROOM

Later —

TUM-TEE-TUM . . .

ERK!

CLUMP CLUMP

ERK!

CAN'T HAVE YOU BARKING AND WAKING TEACHER.

SILENCE

Next —

JINGLE CLATTER VROOM

JINGLE

MILK

MILK

WAH!

HEY! WHERE DID MY DRILL GO?

SNATCH

SNATCH

MY PICK'S NICKED!

Much, much later —

YAWN! THOSE WORKMEN CHASED US FOR MILES, BUT AT LEAST THEY DIDN'T WAKE TEACHER!

Next morning —

GROAN! WE WORKED HARDER YESTERDAY THAN WE DO IN CLASS!

YAWN

YAWN

DARE YOU INVESTIGATE THE STRANGE, SCARY, CREEPY WORLD OF THE BEANO?

THE LOCH NESS MONSTER

HORRIBLE WEEDY NIFF!

LIFT!

POND PONG

SCHOOL POND

UNIDENTIFIED FRYING OBJECTS

SIZZLE

SLURP! SLOO!

YUK!

GROO!

OIL

P S

SIZZLE

THE LOST CITY OF ATLANTA

NOPE! I JUST CAN'T FIND IT!

MAP

B-FILES
(UNEXPLAINED MYSTERIES)

ON YOUR BIKE!

MEET IVOR PUNCTURE — HE'S COME TO GIVE YOU YOUR CYCLING PROFICIENCY TEST.

SNORE!

BZZZZ!

KICK!

BEANO

WHAT ON EARTH IS THAT?

IT'S A MOUNTAIN BIKE MY DAD MADE FOR ME.

RUMBLE!

IT DOESN'T WORK VERY WELL, THOUGH.

OOF!

PROD

TOPPLE!

I'M READY TO START NOW.

Dim eyed 'Erbert

THESE CONES LOOK GREAT.

GRAB!

ZOOM!

IDEAL FOR EATING ICE-CREAM OUT OF.

SLOP!

SLOP!

SLURP!

ZOOM!

Enter Winston, the Janitor's cat—

SQUEEEK!

ZOOM!

ZOOM!

AMAZING!

PERFECT EMERGENCY STOP!

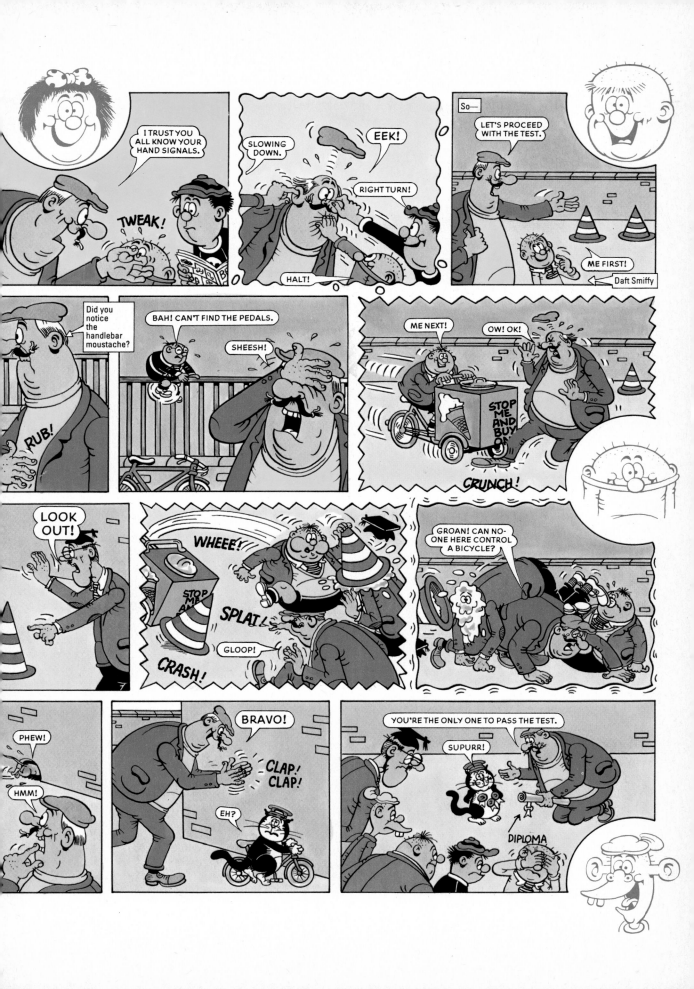

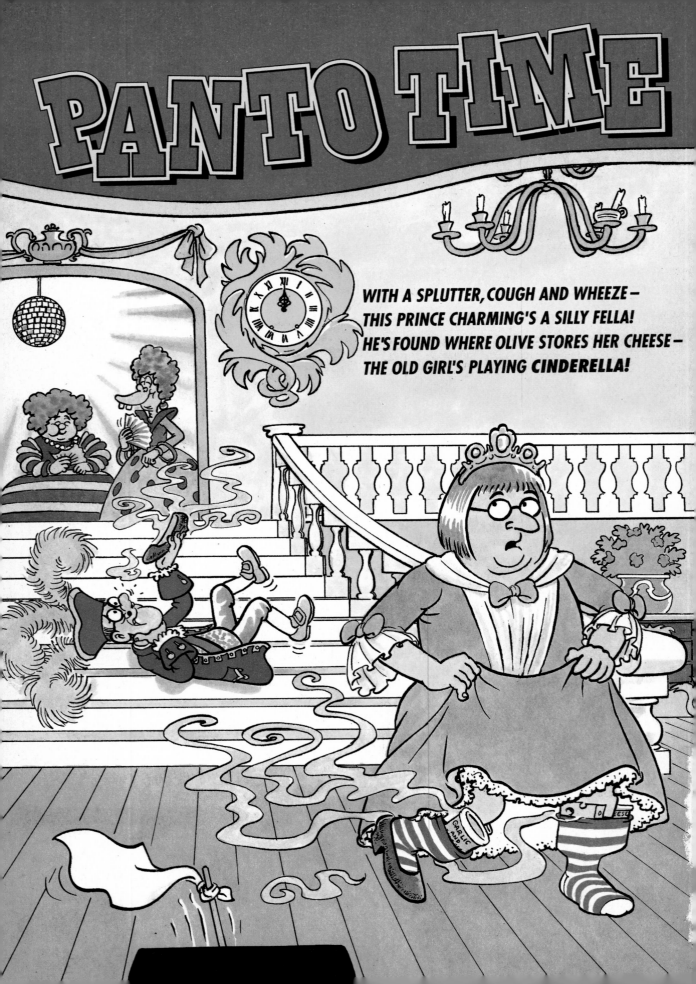

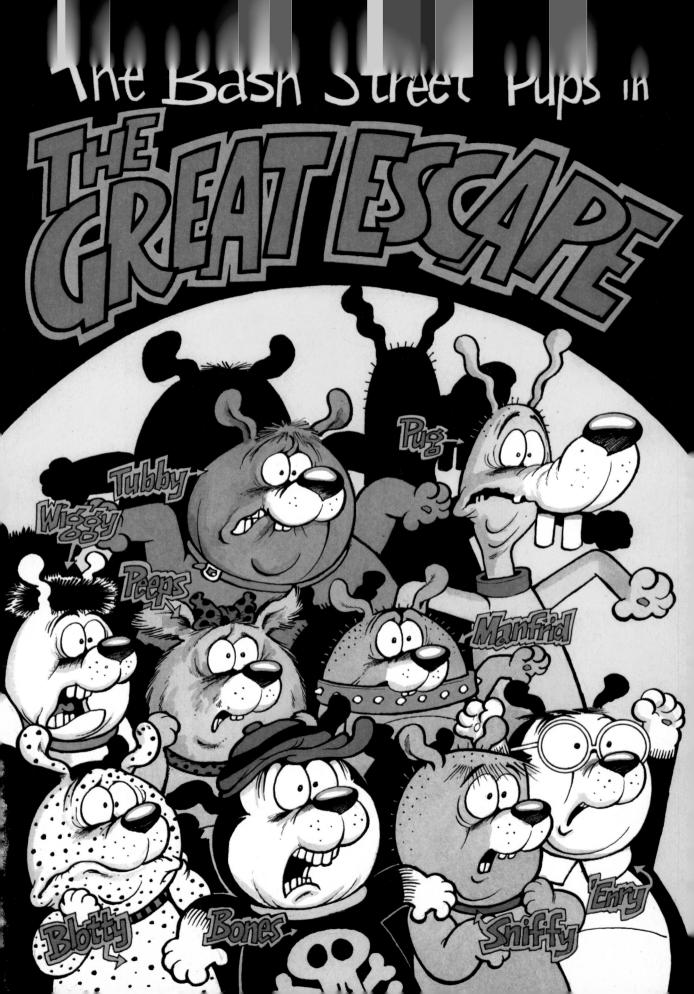

PANTO TIME

THIS KID, HE SPLATTERS HIS HAIR IN GEL,
'COS HE'S GOT A PART – NOT THE LEAST.
WHICH ROLE DOES HE PLAY? I'M SURE YOU CAN TELL,
IS PLUG **BEAUTY** OR IS HE **THE BEAST**?

COLD COMFORT

In class —

AH —

BZZZZ

JOTTER →

NO, WE WON'T. WE CAN CURE HIM! WE HAVE THE TECHNO — TECHYLOG — ER, KNOW-HOW — I THINK.

SNIFF! WHAT ARE YOU GOING TO DO?

WE'RE GOING TO SWEAT THE COLD OUT OF YOU.

THESE VINDALOO PEPPERS SHOULD HEAT PLUG UP.

WE NEED THE POT AT LEAST.

THIS WON'T GET RID OF MY COLD — MY CLOTHES ARE SOAKING!

HE'S RIGHT!

SNIFF SNIFF

In the boiler house —

STOKE IT UP AND WE'LL DRY PLUG OFF.

BOILER

SNIFF SNIFF

S H I S S T E A M H

BOILER

WHAAT? A HOLIDAY FROM SCHOOL!

QUICK! BREATHE ON US!

SORRY, PALS . . .

. . . MY COLD'S CURED!

I'VE AN IDEA!

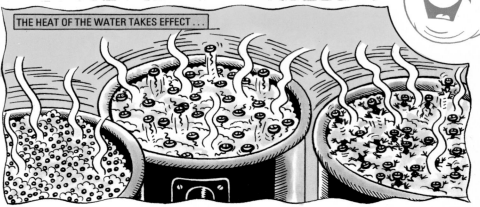

FOLLOW THAT TEACHER...

PART 3

GURGLE!

YAHOO! BETTER THAN THE WATER SLIDES, THAT!

ULP! THEY'LL CATCH ME . . .

. . . UNLESS . . .

GOT IT!

VAROOM!

HMM! WE'LL BUILD A BOAT!

THIS WON'T KEEP UP WITH A SPEEDBOAT.

So —

DON'T FORGET YOUR SEASICK PILLS, READERS.

5

FOLLOW THAT TEACHER...

PART 4

PRANG!

A GOOD GLUTTON ALWAYS CARRIES STRAWS IN CASE OF EMERGENCY.

SUCK!

One gigantic BURP later —

ZOOM!

BURP!

OO-ER!

PLOP!

PLONK!

PLONK!

OH, NO! WHAT ARE WE GOING TO DO NOW?

I KNOW!

ALL THE FUN OF REPAIR

FOR YOUR EARS ONLY

I'M CALLING AN EXTRA-SPECIAL SECRET MEETING.

BANG! BANG!

So—

OMINOUS CREAKING

RIGHT . . .

SECRET MEETING IN PROGRESS

BEND

HOLD ON, DANNY — THIS ISN'T VERY SECRET FOR A SECRET MEETING.

SECRET MEETING IN PROGRESS

Soon—

TIME TO STOKE THE BOILER.

STOP! I'M NOT COAL— I'M WILFRID!

LIFT

BOILER HOUSE

GRR!

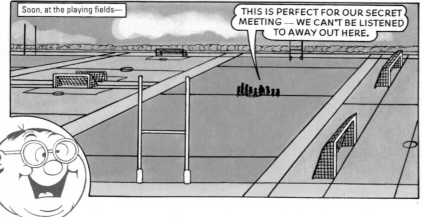

Soon, at the playing fields—

THIS IS PERFECT FOR OUR SECRET MEETING — WE CAN'T BE LISTENED TO AWAY OUT HERE.

HERE'S THE PLAN— WE'RE PLAYING TRUANT TODAY.

FARCE OF THE YEAR SHOW

BASH STREET SHOWJUMPING COMPETITION

OODLES OF PRIZES

THAT GIVES ME AN IDEA.

At the playing fields —

LET ME TRAIN HIM — I'M AN EXPERT ON SHOW-JUMPING.

THIS, I'VE GOT TO SEE.

IT'LL NEVER WIN.

FIRST, I SHOW YOU THE FENCE, HORSE . . .

. . . AND THE YOU JUMP.

JUMP!

I KNEW IT!

I'M NEXT!

PRAY!

NO CHANCE AT ALL.

YOU'RE TOO HEAVY, FATTY.

NONSENSE — THE HORSE JUST NEEDS BUILT UP — THAT'S ALL.

FLUMP!

At the competition —

NEXT, ARE THE BASH ST. KIDS ON "CHUBBY CUDDY".

BASH STREET SHOWJUMPING COMPETITION

JUDGE

BOUNCE!

EH?

BOING!

BOING!

WE'LL HIRE A HORSE, TRAIN IT AND WIN LOTS OF PRIZES.

CHINK!

SHAKE!

SHAKE!

WAH!

SO KIND OF YOU TO CONTRIBUTE, CUTHBERT!

At Honest John's, used horse hirer —

THIS IS ALL YOU GET FOR 18p AND A HALF-SUCKED TOFFEE.

HMPH!

HOLD!

STABLES

THAT HORSE IS AS THICK AS SMIFFY.

MY TURN NOW.

EVEN LESS CHANCE OF WINNING.

TUG!

JUMP!

CRASH!

JUMP!

CRASH!

IT'S ALSO AS SHORT-SIGHTED AS 'ERBERT.

SEE?

—

EAT UP, HORSEY.

CHOMP!

TUG!

But —

ERK! I THINK WE OVERDID THE FEEDING!

BOILK!

NOT TO WORRY — WE CAN STILL WIN.

BOING!

BOUNCE!

OIING!

PUFF! PANT!

Later —

GUESS WHAT? WE WON!

HOW DID THEY DO IT? HOW? HUH?

5

PANTO TIME

"DON'T WORRY! IT'S UTTERLY HARMLESS."
SAY THE KIDS TO ONE WORRIED OLD MAN.
AS THEY SHOVE TEACHER UP IN HARNESS,
FOR HIS PART IN THE SHOW PETER PAN.

M-MUST HAVE BEEN THAT LAST PIE I ATE — THE FIRST FIFTEEN WERE OK! BOAK!

WHAT DID I DO TO DESERVE THIS LOT?

THE "GREEN" ISSUE IS ABOUT CLEAN AIR, WATER — IN FACT, THE ENVIRONMENT — WHO CAN TELL ME ABOUT THE "GREENHOUSE" EFFECT?

WE KNOW WHAT YOU MEAN!

FAN

AIR POLLUTION IS THE CAUSE — PEOPLE CAN HELP BY USING LEAD-FREE PETROL IN CARS!

WE CAN HELP . . .

BLOW

BREAK

STAB

STAB

STAB

STAB

OWOWOWOW!

EH?

RECYCLING THE PAPER MAKES IT ALL MARKED!

IT D-DIDN'T DO ME MUCH G-GOOD, EITHER!

FRYING TODAY

FISH & CHIPS

FISH AND CHIPS WOULDN'T TASTE NEARLY AS NICE WITHOUT THIS "ACID RAIN" — VINEGAR!

HAVING A STRANGE FEELING

SHAKE

SALT

SO THIS "ACID RAIN" MUST BE VERY, VERY GOOD — RIGHT?

SO I MUST BE VERY, VERY SILLY — AND THAT IS RIGHT!

CHOMP

CHEW

LOOK BACK IN ANGER

I SHALL PUT SUMS ON THE BOARD FOR YOU TO COPY AND DO THIS EVENING.

So —

HEH-HEH! SAFE!

Then —

WHIRRRRR!

EH?

Later —

AHA! THESE WILL PUT A STOP TO YOU PELTING ME! I CAN SEE BEHIND!

WING MIRRORS ↓

DAZZLE

DAZZLE

DAZZLE

WAA!

But then —

THAT'S WHERE YOU'RE WRONG!

EEH!

GASP!

YOU'LL NEVER KNOW IF I'M WATCHING YOU OR HAVE MY BACK TURNED! TITTER! I'M A GENIUS!

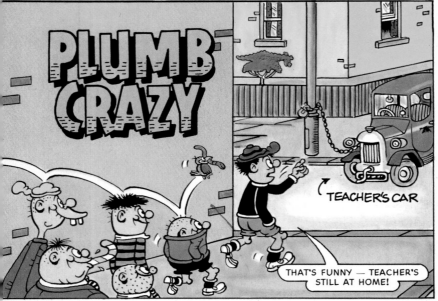

PLUMB CRAZY

TEACHER'S CAR

THAT'S FUNNY — TEACHER'S STILL AT HOME!

Suddenly —

AAATISHOO!

GET UP! YOU'RE TAKING CLASS IIB TODAY!

EH? ME... BUT... ER... YOUR HEADSHIP — I'LL BE GOOD FROM NOW ON!

PLOP

SCRAPE

SLIDE

In class IIB —

AHEM! WHAT TO DO FIRST! ER...

...A CUP OF TEA! I ALWAYS START THE DAY WITH A CUP OF TEA! SLOO!

POUR

SUGAR

MILK

...LEFT HAND THREADED 13MM PIPE...

THIS WAY, KIDS!

Later —

WE'VE HAD A GO AT SOME PRACTICAL WORK, SIR.

EH? VERY GOOD! WHAT WORK?

WE'VE TAKEN OUT THE WATER RADIATOR AND USED CUTHBERT'S TROUSERS INSTEAD!

EEK!

EXPAND

SW

SPL

HISS

GUR

Then —

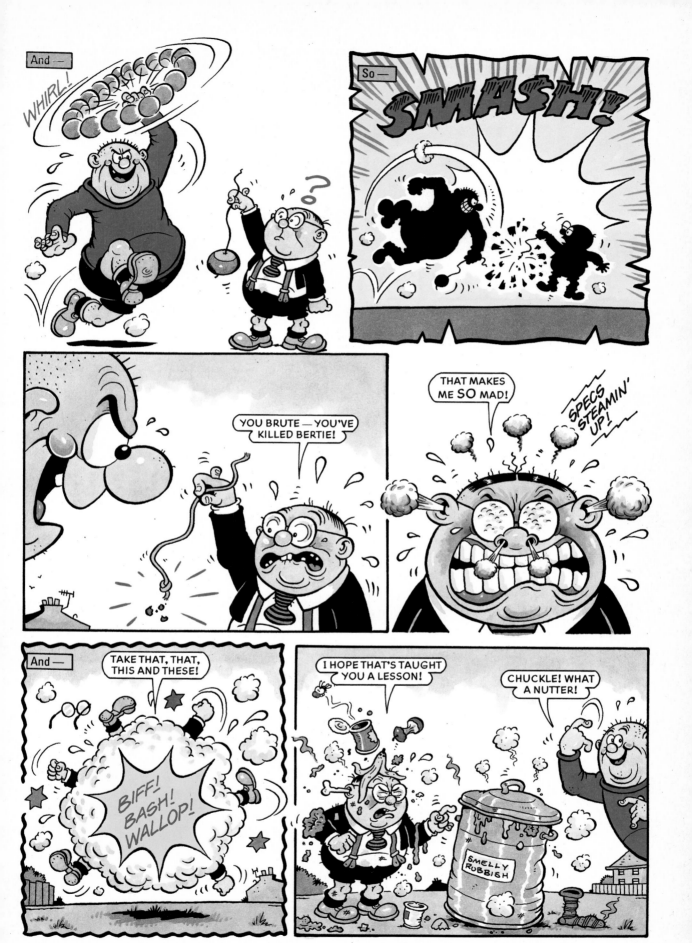